ABOUT THE

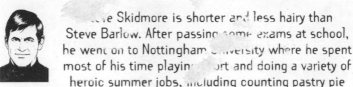

... and
...or,
...d
... at a
...an writing
together. ...sails a boat
named Which ...ally hasn't a clue

...e Skidmore is shorter and less hairy than Steve Barlow. After passing some exams at school, he went on to Nottingham University where he spent most of his time playing ...ort and doing a variety of heroic summer jobs, including counting pastry pie lids (honest). He trained as a teacher of Drama, English and Film Studies, before teaming up with Steve Barlow to become a full-time author.

Together they have written many books, including:
The Mad Myths series
Find out more at:
www.the2steves.net

ABOUT THE ILLUSTRATOR

Sonia Leong is based in Cambridge, in the UK, and is a super-star manga artist. She won Tokyopop's first UK Rising Stars of Manga competition (2005-06) and her first graphic novel was Manga Shakespeare: Romeo and Juliet. She's a member of Sweatdrop Studios and has too many awards to fit in this teeny space.
Find Sonia at her website: www.fyredrake.net

I HERO

Dragon Slayer

Steve Barlow and Steve Skidmore
Illustrated by Sonia Leong

EDGE
FRANKLIN WATTS

LONDON·SYDNEY

First published in 2010
by Franklin Watts

Text © Steve Barlow and Steve Skidmore 2010
Illustrations © Sonia Leong 2010
Cover design by Jonathan Hair

Franklin Watts
338 Euston Road
London NW1 3BH

Franklin Watts Australia
Level 17/207 Kent Street
Sydney, NSW 2000

A CIP catalogue record for this book
is available from the British Library.

ISBN: 978 0 7496 9678 8

1 3 5 7 9 10 8 6 4 2

Printed in Great Britain

Franklin Watts is a division of Hachette Children's Books,
an Hachette UK company.
www.hachette.co.uk

Decide your own destiny...

This book is not like others you may have read. You are the hero of this adventure. It is up to you to make decisions that will affect how the adventure unfolds.

Each section of this book is numbered. At the end of most sections, you will have to make a choice. The choice you make will take you to a different section of the book.

Some of your choices will help you to complete the adventure successfully. But choose carefully, some of your decisions could be fatal!

If you fail, then start the adventure again and learn from your mistake.

If you choose correctly you will succeed in your adventure.

Don't be a zero, be a hero!

You are a warrior from the land of Scanda. Lord Danu is the ruler of your people.

You are a monster slayer. You have fought wolves and wild boars, the walrus and the killer whale, brown bears of the forests and white bears of the snow-lands. You have battled against ogres and giants. But you have never yet tested your strength against the creature that all your people fear – a dragon.

Your latest mission was to slay a giant. You are sailing home in your longship bearing its head as a trophy for your Lord. Though both you and your men are weary, you are pleased with your success.

Now turn to section 1.

1

As your ship sails between your land and the kingdom of Halund, you see a glow in the sky.

The night is misty. Rain lashes the deck. The ship is pitching and rolling in a stormy sea and you can see little of the land.

The ship's master joins you. "King Olaf's great Golden Hall lies in that direction. Perhaps his people have lit a beacon, calling for help. Shall we change course?"

If you wish to investigate the source of the glow, go to 39.

If you decide to ignore it and go on your way, turn to 44.

2

You prowl around the hall. Your men are all asleep by now. They stir fitfully as the noise made by your armour disturbs them.

You stop moving, and wait. But the heavy armour continues to weigh you down, and your eyelids droop as tiredness steals over you. Soon, you are asleep.

Go to 7.

3

"Thank you," you say, "you are loyal friends. As you offer your help freely, I gladly accept it. I shall have need of friends tonight."

Night falls. Hours pass, but the dragon does not appear. Your eyelids grow heavy. Your men are already asleep. You wonder whether you should sleep also, to conserve your strength for the battle that lies ahead.

If you want to go to sleep, go to 7.
If you decide to remain awake, go to 16.

4

As you prepare to leave in search of the wounded dragon, an old man, one of King Olaf's attendants, stops you.

"Sir," he says, "I was a warrior once, and a notable beast slayer in my own time. I can give you good advice on fighting a dragon."

You laugh. "I have already fought a dragon without your advice."

The old man's eyes glitter. "Beware of pride that scorns wise counsel. Will you listen?"

If you choose to listen to what the old warrior has to say, go to 42.

If you have no time to listen to an old man's ramblings, go to 25.

5

The harbour master leads you to King Olaf. The King was a mighty warrior once, but now he is old: his hair is white and his strength has failed him.

You find the King in his great Golden Hall – but the hall is devastated. The proud banners hang in shreds. The stone and timber of the floor and walls are cracked and scorched by fire.

King Olaf is standing over a man from your country. The man is clearly a captive, held in chains.

The King is beside himself with rage. "Greedy fool!" he cries. "You have doomed us all!" He turns to his guards. "Kill him!"

If you wish to fight to protect your countryman, go to 13.

If you wish to beg King Olaf for the man's life, go to 24.

6

The underwater passage that leads out of the pool is long and hard. Several times, you try to rise to the surface. Each time, your head meets only rock. You rise one last time – and find clear air above your head.

You are in a cave. It is lit by a strange red glow from a pool of fire. To one side of this lies a mountain of gold – the dragon's hoard. At the other lies the dragon you fought in the Golden Hall, lying in a pool of its own blood.

At the water's edge is the body of a warrior – perhaps some former seeker of the dragon's treasure. The man's armour is half melted, but he holds a sword in his bony hand.

You heave yourself out of the pool.

If you want to inspect the dragon's hoard, go to 41.

If you want to inspect the dead warrior, go to 38.

If you want to inspect the dragon, go to 22.

7

You sleep soundly until a noise disturbs you.
You awake with a start and stare into two
dreadful, glowing reptilian eyes. The dragon
has crept silently into the hall as you slept.

The dragon rears its head. You try to dodge
but your heavy armour weighs you down.
Dragon-fire washes over you. Your chain-link
mailshirt becomes a skin-tight furnace. You
scream as your hair bursts into flames and your
eyeballs boil in their sockets.

Death is a welcome release from pain.

**You have failed. If you wish to begin the
adventure again, go back to 1.**

8

You draw your sword and rush forward to save
your friend.

But the dragon spots you immediately. It
rakes the sleeping man's body with its powerful
talons, killing him instantly. Then, with snake-
like speed, it strikes at you.

The terrible jaws snap at your unprotected
body. The first bite almost tears you in half. The

second bite silences your screams forever.

You have failed and left your companions unprotected.

If you wish to start your adventure again, go to 1.

9

You push roughly past the harbour master. "Out of my way, slave!" you cry.

The harbour master blocks your way with his spear. "I am no slave – and no stranger shall pass without the King's permission. Guards! Guards!"

If you decide to make a hurried apology, go to 17.

If you decide to fight the guards, go to 13.

10

Wulf is beside himself with rage at your refusal. "Arrogant upstart!" he cries. "First you humiliate me before my King, now you scorn my help. The dragon is dead, and now you will join him!" He draws his sword.

Go to 13.

11

You shake your head. "Wulf is right about one thing. I must see the beast with my own eyes before I will believe that it is truly dead. It must have gone into the pool, and to find out what has happened to it, I must follow."

Your men are horrified. "Are you mad? You'll freeze! You'll drown! It's certain death!"

If you agree to give up the search and return to King Olaf, go to 18.

If you ignore your companions' advice and prepare to dive into the pool, go to 37.

12

You draw your sword and hurl yourself at the dragon. You hack at its body with all your strength, but the glittering scales are too hard.

The dragon roars with fury and strikes at you, but you dodge and strike again.

This time, the sword shatters in your hand, leaving you weaponless.

If you decide to continue the fight bare-handed, go to 36.

If you choose to try to save yourself, go to 19.

13

"To arms, men!" you cry.

King Olaf's guards rush towards you, swords raised. You have few companions. They fight bravely, but you are heavily outnumbered. One by one, your men are cut down. For a moment, you fight on alone – then you, too, fall beneath the slashing blades.

Your arrogance has cost you your life.

If you wish to begin the adventure again, go to 1.

14

You rush to the side of the dead dragon. With a supreme effort, you wrestle the Black Spear from beneath its leg.

The greatest weapon of King Olaf's folk may yet save you from the savagery of the dragon – if you use it wisely!

If you attack the dragon and stab it with the spear, go to 26.

If you wedge the end of the spear against a rock and wait for the dragon's charge, go to 30.

15

"King Olaf," you say, "your enemy is my enemy. I shall not leave until the dragon is defeated."

"Brave words!" sneers a voice. The speaker is Wulf, one of King Olaf's warriors. "I heard that you challenged Gond Hammerfist to a swimming match – and he won easily! You're nothing but a braggart and a weakling!" King Olaf glares at Wulf, but his men mutter and give you unfriendly looks.

You cannot ignore Wulf's challenge.

If you want to reply to Wulf, go to 29.

If you want to call your men to fight to avenge your honour, go to 13.

16

You know that you must remain alert.

Your armour is heavy and taking it off would help you to remain awake. You would also move more quietly without it.

On the other hand, without its protection you would be defenceless against the dragon.

If you want to take off your armour, go to 23.

If you want to keep it on, go to 2.

17

"My friend," you tell the harbour master in soothing tones, "we are not here to steal or to mock. We saw a fire and feared that some disaster had befallen our friend King Olaf. I am here to find out what has happened, and to help you if I can."

The harbour master lowers his spear. "I apologise for my ill manners. Disaster has indeed come to us. I will take you to King Olaf."

Go to 5.

18

When he hears how your quest has ended, King Olaf is overjoyed. "With such a wound," he cries, "the creature can never survive!"

That night, the Golden Hall is once more filled with noise and light. Bards sing of brave deeds. Whole oxen and wild boar roast over crackling fires. Mugs of mead and ale are lifted in celebration.

But in the midst of all the rejoicing, a dark shadow settles over the hall. All around there are cries of "Dragon! Dragon!" You are astounded – surely the dragon is dead?

The roof groans for a moment – then collapses. Fire pours through the crumbling walls as though a volcano is erupting outside. You are buried beneath blazing timbers as King Olaf's great Golden Hall falls into ruin all around you.

Your adventure has ended. If you wish to begin again, turn to 1.

19

You drop your broken sword and turn to run. The dragon leaps in pursuit. Its fiery breath scorches your cheek as you dodge.

Your men are waking with shouts of alarm as they realise that the enemy is upon them!

If you choose to leave your men to fight the dragon and save yourself, go to 28.

If you decide to call your men to help you fight the dragon, go to 45.

If you want to tell your men to stand back while you attack the beast with your bare hands, go to 36.

20

"I am sorry, men," you say, "I cannot allow you to share this danger."

You send your men from the hall. They leave reluctantly, with many a backward glance and shake of the head.

Night falls, but there is no sign of the dragon. Hours pass and your eyelids grow heavy. With no companions to help, soon you are asleep.

Go to 7.

21

"King Olaf," you say, "I have come here to help you in your hour of need. It would be a pity to begin my quest with the death of one of my countrymen. I ask you to spare him."

The King considers. "For the sake of your friendship, and that of your master, Lord Danu, I will. Take him to prison," he tells his guards. "We may need him later."

If you decide to speak to the man whose life you have saved, go to 35.

If you wish to leave him in prison and go with King Olaf, go to 31.

22

As soon as you draw close to the dragon, you realise that it is dead. Its eyes are shut and it is not breathing. One leg rests on the shaft of the famous Black Spear it stole from King Olaf's Golden Hall.

A roar brings you to your feet. Another dragon, three times the size of the dead one, slithers into view. The dragon you killed was only a youngster. This is the mother dragon, and she wants revenge!

If you choose to dive back into the pool to escape, go to 49.

If you decide to attack the mother dragon, go to 32.

23

You decide that armour will not help you.
Dragons breathe fire, not arrows. It is better to
be able to dodge. The moment you take it off,
you feel ready for anything.

For some time, nothing happens. Then
you hear the sounds of stealthy movement.
A shadow falls upon your companions. The
dragon has entered the hall!

The beast is as long as your ship. It has
green-grey scales and terrible bat-like wings. Its
red eyes glow with inner fire. Its body snakes
forward on four powerful legs.

It creeps forward until one of your
companions lies helpless at its feet.

**If you decide to attack the dragon and save
your companion, go to 8.**

**If you decide to remain still and play dead,
go to 40.**

24

"I do not know what this man has done," you say, "but I beg you to spare his life."

"You do not know what you ask," the King replies. "A terrible fire-breathing dragon came in the night. It burned my hall, killed my men and stole our greatest treasure – the Black Spear of Halund. Just before daybreak, it flew away – but I have no doubt it will return tonight. And it was all the fault of this wretch." King Olaf points at his prisoner. "He stole a cup from the dragon's golden hoard. The dragon attacked us in revenge."

If you decide that the man deserves to die, and you will not interfere, go to 48.

If you wish to continue to plead for the man's life, go to 21.

25

As you are about to leave, Wulf appears with some of King Olaf's guards.

"We will go with you," he says. "I will see the beast dead with my own eyes, or I will not believe that you have truly overcome it."

You grit your teeth at Wulf's insulting words, but his demand is reasonable.

Tracking the blood that has dropped from the dragon's wound during its headlong flight, you travel through marshes and across dark, brooding hills. The trail ends beside a dark pool surrounded by stunted trees that grow out of the bare rock. Their leafless branches glitter with frost.

"The beast has crawled into the water to die," says one of your men. "Let's claim our reward."

If you agree with your companion and decide to return to King Olaf, go to 18.

If you choose to search the pool, go to 11.

26

You stab at the dragon's flank with all your might, but you are not strong enough to force the spear through the dragon's hard scales. The spear is undamaged, but you cannot use it to defeat the dragon.

If you decide to flee, go to 49.

If you decide to tackle the dragon with your bare hands, as you did its child, go to 34.

27

Your attempts to explain why you did not help King Olaf meet with a furious response.

"I will hear no excuses!" roars Lord Danu. "I have given you many gifts – bright swords, strong shields, armour fit for a king – and this is how you repay me! You call yourself a dragon slayer? You are no better than a coward! Get out of my sight!"

You have failed before your quest has even begun. To start again, turn back to 1.

28

Your men rush to your aid. But none of their weapons can penetrate the creature's scales. They fall one by one, torn apart by jaws or talons, or shrivelled by the dragon's fiery breath, until only you are left.

To fight on is hopeless. You let your arms fall to your sides and wait for the end. It is not long in coming. Dragon-fire burns you to ashes where you stand.

You have failed. If you wish to begin the adventure again, turn to 1.

29

"Did you also hear," you ask Wulf, "that I was leading the race when a sea-serpent attacked me and dragged me down into the black depths? But I slew him – and six more of his kind. Have you done such a deed, Wulf? If you are so keen to slay monsters, why did you not tackle this dragon as it ravaged your master's hall? Perhaps it is you who are the weakling!"

Wulf glares at you and says nothing.

King Olaf raises a hand. "Enough! We should be friends and fight together." He turns to you and to Wulf. "Shake hands and forget your differences."

If you wish to shake Wulf's hand, go to 33.
If you refuse to shake Wulf's hand, go to 46.

30

You kneel and settle the butt of the spear against a rock. You hold the spear point towards the dragon, and wait.

With a roar of fury, the dragon charges. You know you must not flinch.

The dragon is so intent on tearing you to

pieces, it does not notice the spear. As it rears to strike, it runs onto the deadly blade. The head of the spear disappears inside its great body. The dragon gives a single howl of agony that makes the rocky walls tremble, and falls to the ground, pierced to the heart.

You were not powerful enough to slay the dragon yourself, but you were clever enough to use the dragon's great strength against it.

Go to 50.

31

You kneel before King Olaf. "I am ready to protect your hall. My Lord Danu is your friend and ally. I shall fight the dragon if it returns."

The King shakes his head. "You are a brave man. But the dragon is too powerful for human strength. I will send no man to a needless death."

If you want to accept King Olaf's offer and go home, go to 27.

If you still decide to defend King Olaf's hall and fight the dragon, go to 15.

32

You race to the attack. The dragon breathes fire at you – but your sudden charge is so unexpected that the burst of flame misses.

You raise the borrowed sword and bring it down on the dragon's shoulder with all your might. But the blade instantly shatters. The sword Wulf gave you has proved to be brittle and worthless – as no doubt he knew – and it has failed you.

If you want to take the dead warrior's sword, go to 43.

If you want to take the spear from the dead dragon, go to 14.

33

"Harsh words break no bones," you say. You offer Wulf your hand. Scowling, he takes it.

"Come," says King Olaf, "we must make plans."

You spend the day deciding how you will deal with the deadly beast that has brought destruction to King Olaf's hall.

As night falls, the King wishes you well and leads his men to safety.

Your companions do not wish to leave. "We cannot allow you to face this danger alone," they say. "We will stay with you tonight in the Golden Hall."

If you decide you must fight the dragon alone, go to 20.

If you decide to accept your companions' help, go to 3.

34

You hurl yourself at the dragon, gripping it around the neck as you did before with its offspring.

But this is no half-grown youngster. The old she-dragon is strong and wily.

Your arms do not even stretch around her neck, so your strangle-hold does not work. The creature shakes like a dog drying its coat, and hurls you across the cave to land, winded, on the stone floor.

You do not even have time to get to your feet before the dragon's fiery breath blasts you into oblivion.

If you wish to begin the adventure again, go to 1.

35

"Speak!" you tell the prisoner. "Why did you steal from the dragon's hoard?"

"I was running away," moans the slave. "My master was going to beat me. I did not look where I was going. I fell into a pool, and somehow found myself in a cave filled with gold. There was no guard, so I thought the hoard must have been abandoned. I took the cup for my master, hoping that he would forgive me."

You leave the slave in prison, but now you know that the way to the dragon's lair lies through a pool.

Go to 31.

36

You fling yourself at the dragon's long neck and begin to squeeze.

The dragon's fire cannot reach you here, but it tries to tear at you with its terrible claws.

You let go of the neck and grab both the creature's horns. You force them apart with all your strength. The dragon bellows in pain and fury. Veins stand out on your neck and forehead. You give one final, despairing heave.

With a ghastly wrenching and a spray of dark blood, you tear the dragon's left horn from its head.

You hold the grisly trophy aloft in triumph as the wounded beast screeches in agony. Defeated, the dragon bursts through the great doors of the Golden Hall and flies off into the night.

If you want to pursue the wounded dragon, go to 4.

If you decide to let it escape, go to 18.

37

As you stand on the brink of the pool, Wulf approaches you.

"Perhaps I have misjudged you," he says. "You broke your sword in the fight with the dragon. Please do me the honour of taking mine. It is a noble weapon and I'm sure it will serve you well."

If you wish to accept Wulf's offer, go to 47.
If you decide to refuse it, go to 10.

38

From the old-fashioned look of the warrior's weapons and armour, he has been dead for years. He was clearly a mighty man in life, but all his strength could not save him.

You hear a noise and straighten up. An enormous dragon, three times the size of the one you defeated, emerges from behind the hoard. You realise with horror that this is the mother dragon whose child you have killed.

If you choose to dive back into the pool to escape, go to 49.

If you decide to attack the mother dragon, go to 32.

39

By the time you reach the harbour of Halund, it is dawn. The sky is overcast and a glow still lights the grey clouds from beneath.

As your ship comes alongside the quay, the harbour master challenges you. "Who are you, stranger? Have you come to steal whatever the forces of darkness have left us? To mock us in our sorrow? You shall not pass!"

If you decide to ignore this insolence and push past the man, go to 9.

If you wish to explain why you have come, go to 17.

40

Your instinct is to save your companion, but you know you cannot help him. The dragon will spot you instantly if you move. There is no point in throwing your life away for nothing.

You force yourself to remain still as the terrible beast tears your companion from neck to waist with its sword-sharp talons, killing him without a sound.

But as the dragon bends its neck to feed, it is no longer looking in your direction. You take the opportunity to leap into action.

If you want to attack the dragon with your sword, go to 12.

If you choose to attack with your bare hands, go to 36.

41

You cross the floor of the cave to the hoard.

Gleaming in the light of the unnatural fire lie treasures without number. There are plates, bowls and drinking cups made of gold and precious jewels; rings, brooches and necklaces; arm bands and bracelets; all lying like islands in a sea of coins.

You pick up a great golden bowl. You are so intent on the treasure that you do not notice the stealthy footfalls behind you as the mother dragon, whose child you have slain, prepares to take her revenge.

Go to 49.

42

"What have you to say to me?" you ask.

"No sword can cut through the dragon's scales," the old man tells you. "There is no beast as powerful as a dragon. You must use its own strength against it."

You think carefully about the old warrior's words.

Go to 25.

43

You snatch up the sword from the dead warrior's hand.

The dragon charges towards you and you return furiously to the attack – but the sword blade rebounds time and time again from the armoured hide until it, too, shatters.

You despair as you realise that no sword can injure the dragon.

If you choose to flee, go to 49.

If you decide to tackle the dragon with your bare hands, as you did its child, go to 34.

44

You return to the court and report your success against the giant to Lord Danu. He calls you the best of warriors, and promises you a rich reward.

But when you tell him what you saw as you sailed past the coast of Halund, he is displeased.

"You should have gone at once to find out the cause of the blaze," he says. "King Olaf is our friend and ally. Some terrible misfortune may have befallen his people." He stands, and in a voice of command cries, "Sail for Halund at once. Take your best men, and offer King Olaf any aid you can!"

If you refuse because you are tired from your recent struggle with the giant, go to 27.

If you decide to gather your men and set off, go to 39.

45

"Men!" you cry. "Attack! Kill the foul beast!"

As your men obey, you slip out through the great doors to the hall. You close them behind you and wedge them shut.

Tears stream from your eyes as flames leap from the doomed hall. You listen to the clashing of swords on scales and the screams of your men as they are ripped to pieces.

You are no hero. You are a coward. If you wish to begin the adventure again, turn to 1.

46

Angrily, you shake your head. "Wulf has insulted me. I refuse to fight with a liar and a coward."

You stride from the hall, followed by your men. But Wulf gathers the King's guards and follows you. He grabs you roughly by the arm.

"You have offended my master, King Olaf," he cries. "Stand and fight, if you are a man!"

If you decide to fight, go to 13.

If you decide to walk away, go home and report Wulf's insults to Lord Danu, go to 27.

47

"Thank you, Wulf, my friend," you answer.
"I am glad all is now well between us." As you
say this, a look of savage glee crosses Wulf's
face. You wonder whether you were right to
trust him.

But it is too late for second thoughts. With
the borrowed sword strapped to your back, you
take a deep breath and dive into the pool.

Go to 6.

48

You shrug your shoulders. "Let justice be done."

The captain of the guards signals two of his men to hold the prisoner. He strides forward, raising his sword.

A moment later, it is all over. The man's headless corpse slumps to the floor, blood spurting from the severed neck.

King Olaf has executed your countryman. This is a serious matter! What will you do now?

If you decide to go home and report the death to Lord Danu, turn to 27.

If you still wish to help King Olaf, go to 31.

49

You turn to flee. But the mother dragon is too fast for you. Flame blossoms around you. Searing pain tears through you as the blood in your veins turns to steam and the skin is stripped from your back. Then merciful darkness overcomes you as the dragon-fire burns you to ashes as you run.

If you wish to begin the adventure again, return to 1.

50

Your men are overjoyed when you emerge from the pool. Only Wulf seems less than pleased with your success. You know that one day there will be a reckoning between you and Wulf – but not today.

You order King Olaf's men to carry the treasures of the dragon's hoard back to the Golden Hall.

When you report your success, King Olaf's gratitude knows no bounds. Every night for a month, the Golden Hall echoes with feasting in celebration of your mighty deeds.

When the time comes for you to leave, the King insists on loading your ship with half the dragon's treasure.

Lord Danu greets you on your return. "Welcome, dragon slayer! The whole world has heard of your strength and courage. You have brought fame and glory to my court and the folk of Scanda. You are a hero!"

ARTIST AT WORK!

Hi there! I'm Sonia, and I draw all the artwork in the I HERO books. I work mainly as a manga artist and I run drawing workshops, too.

I draw in three main stages for I HERO. First, I sketch out the rough positions in pencil. Then I make any changes and work up the art in ink. Finally, I add layers of texture for the fills and shadows.

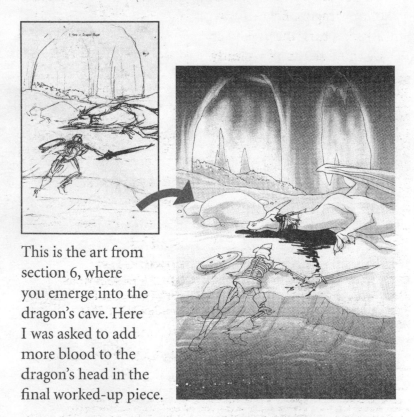

This is the art from section 6, where you emerge into the dragon's cave. Here I was asked to add more blood to the dragon's head in the final worked-up piece.

The art above is from section 8 – I cropped in quite close on the rough, but I wanted to show more of the dragon. Below I was asked to turn the dragon so we could see its head clearly.

1.

2.

Want the chance to see your I HERO fan art* in an I HERO book? Send it to:

**I HERO fan art
EDGE/Franklin Watts
15th Floor, 338 Euston Road,
London NW1 3BH**

or email it to:

ad@hachettechildrens.co.uk

Tomb
Runner

Steve Barlow and Steve Skidmore
Illustrated by Sonia Leong

You are one of the world's leading treasure hunters. Your talent for archaeology is only matched by your skills in martial arts and languages. You have travelled the world searching for, and discovering, priceless treasures and artefacts.

You are in your library, studying an antique map, when your butler enters. He coughs.

"What is it, Peters?" you ask.

"I'm sorry to disturb you," he replies, "but there is a gentleman in the lobby. He wishes to see you. He says it is very important. Here is his card."

Continue reading the adventure in
I HERO Tomb Runner

I HERO
DECIDE YOUR OWN DESTINY
Tomb Runner
Steve Barlow - Steve Skidmore

All these other I HERO titles are available now!